Brazier

C000203823

Mental Maths Tests

for ages 6–7

✓ **Ten complete Mental Maths timed tests, together with a pre-recorded CD**

✓ **Ideal practice for National Tests**

✓ **Bonus material includes record sheets and addition squares**

Introduction

Mental Maths Tests for ages 6–7 is a result of repeated requests from teachers, following the great popularity of *Mental Maths Tests for ages 7–8, 8–9, 9–10* and *10–11*.

Many teachers have found that our tests provide a very useful structure for consolidation lessons. By working through the tests with the pupils, teachers can gain valuable insights into their pupils' levels of performance. At the same time the children are gaining experience of working in a test situation, listening to recorded questions. The questions are timed, allowing the pupils 10 seconds for each of the more straightforward questions, then 15 seconds for the more difficult questions.

General instructions for the administration of the tests

To make these tests seem as realistic as possible children should have clear desks and only a pen or pencil to write with. They should not be supplied with paper for working out the answers.

Before starting each test the children should write their name and school in the spaces provided.

Inform the children that:

- they should work individually and should not talk at all during the test;

- there will be 10 questions altogether;

- they will be allowed 10 seconds to answer each of the first five questions and 15 seconds for each of the next five questions;

- for some questions, some information will be provided on the test sheet;

- calculators or other equipment are not allowed;

- they should not rub out answers but, if they wish to change them, they can cross them out and write their new answers next to the incorrect ones;

- if they cannot do a question they should put a cross in the answer box.

Test 1

Before playing the test on the CD give each child a copy of the test and read out the following script:

Listen to the instructions carefully. I will answer any questions that you have after I have finished reading the instructions to you. Once the test starts you will not be able to ask any questions.

The first question is a practice question. In the test there will then be ten questions.

Each question has an answer box. Make sure that you only write the answer to the correct question in the box. Try to work out each answer in your head. You can make notes outside the answer box if this helps you but do not try to write out calculations because you will not have enough time. For each question you will find important information already provided for you. This information may be numbers or it could be pictures. Look carefully at the information while you listen to the questions.

Each question will be read out twice. Listen carefully then work out your answer. If you cannot do the question, just put a cross. If you make a mistake, do not rub out the wrong answer; cross it out and write the correct answer.

Some questions are easy and some are more difficult. Do not worry if you find a question hard; just do your best. I hope that you enjoy the test.

At this point, answer any questions that the children ask.

Now listen carefully to the practice question. You will hear the question twice, then you will have ten seconds to work out and write down the answer.

What is two add two?

What is two add two?

Allow the children ten seconds to write the answer, then say:

Put your pencil down.

Check that the children have written the answer to the practice question in the practice question answer box. Remind them that they cannot ask any more questions once the test is started. When you are ready, press start on your CD player.

When the test is finished ask the children to stop writing, then collect the test sheets. For ease of marking we have created a copy of the test paper with the answers entered in the appropriate boxes.

Questions for Test 1

For each of the first five questions you have ten seconds to work out and write down the answer.

1 Add six and three.

2 What is ten subtract six?

3 What number is half of ten?

4 Multiply five by three.

5 Round thirty-eight to the nearest ten.

For each of the next questions you have fifteen seconds to work out and write down the answer.

6 Look at the shapes. Two of the shapes have right angles. Tick the shapes that have right angles.

7 Look at the number sequence. Write the next number in the sequence.

8 What is the total of ten and twelve?

9 Look at the numbers. Draw rings around the numbers that are multiples of five.

10 Look at the clock face. Draw the clock hands to show the time three o'clock.

Put your pencil down. The test is over.

Andrew Brodie: Mental Maths Tests 6–7 © A & C Black

Test 1

First name _____ Last name _____

School _____

_____ **Total marks** [   ]

Practice question

| | 2   2 |

Ten-second questions

| **1** | 6   3 |

| **2** | 10   6 |

| **3** | 10 |

| **4** | 5   3 |

| **5** | 38 |

Fifteen-second questions

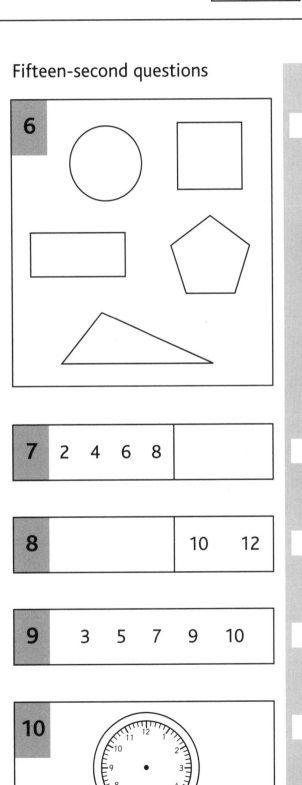

| **6** | |

| **7** | 2   4   6   8 | |

| **8** | 10   12 |

| **9** | 3   5   7   9   10 |

| **10** | |

Test 1 Answers

Practice question

| 4 | 2 | 2 |

Ten-second questions

| 1 | 9 | 6 | 3 |

| 2 | 4 | 10 | 6 |

| 3 | 5 | 10 |

| 4 | 15 | 5 | 3 |

| 5 | 40 | 38 |

Fifteen-second questions

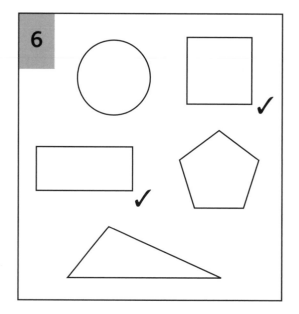

6

| 7 | 2 | 4 | 6 | 8 | **10** |

| 8 | **22** | 10 | 12 |

| 9 | 3 | ⑤ | 7 | 9 | ⑩ |

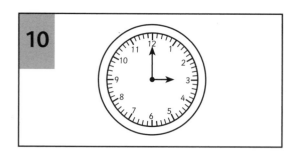

10

Andrew Brodie: Mental Maths Tests 6–7 © A & C Black

Before playing the test on the CD give each child a copy of the test and read out the following script:

> **Listen to the instructions carefully. I will answer any questions that you have after I have finished reading the instructions to you. Once the test starts you will not be able to ask any questions.**
>
> **The first question is a practice question. In the test there will then be ten questions.**
>
> **Each question has an answer box. Make sure that you only write the answer to the correct question in the box. Try to work out each answer in your head. You can make notes outside the answer box if this helps you but do not try to write out calculations because you will not have enough time. For each question you will find important information already provided for you. This information may be numbers or it could be pictures. Look carefully at the information while you listen to the questions.**
>
> **Each question will be read out twice. Listen carefully then work out your answer. If you cannot do the question, just put a cross. If you make a mistake, do not rub out the wrong answer; cross it out and write the correct answer.**
>
> **Some questions are easy and some are more difficult. Do not worry if you find a question hard; just do your best. I hope that you enjoy the test.**

At this point, answer any questions that the children ask.

> **Now listen carefully to the practice question. You will hear the question twice, then you will have ten seconds to work out and write down the answer.**
>
> > *What is five add one?*
>
> > *What is five add one?*

Allow the children ten seconds to write the answer, then say:

> **Put your pencil down.**

Check that the children have written the answer to the practice question in the practice question answer box. Remind them that they cannot ask any more questions once the test is started. When you are ready, press start on your CD player.

When the test is finished ask the children to stop writing, then collect the test sheets. For ease of marking we have created a copy of the test paper with the answers entered in the appropriate boxes.

Questions for Test 2

For each of the first five questions you have ten seconds to work out and write down the answer.

1   What is the total of six and four?

2   What is the difference between fourteen and six?

3   What is six times two?

4   How many more is twenty than sixteen?

5   Add twenty to forty.

For each of the next questions you have fifteen seconds to work out and write down the answer.

6   Look at the tally. What total does it show?

7   Look at the scales. Some apples are being weighed. What is the weight of the apples?

8   What day follows straight after Thursday?

9   Look at the shapes. Two of them are hexagons. Tick the shapes that are hexagons.

10 Look at the clock face. Draw the clock hands to show the time ten o'clock.

Put your pencil down. The test is over.

Andrew Brodie: Mental Maths Tests 6–7 © A & C Black

First name _____ Last name _____

School _____

_____ **Total marks** [   ]

Practice question

| | 5   1 |

Ten-second questions

1	6 4
2	14 6
3	6 2
4	20 16
5	20 40

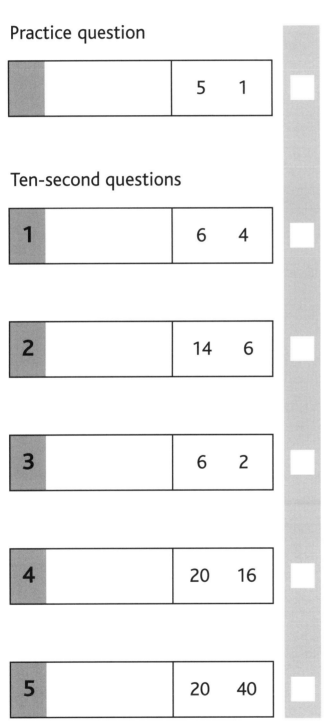

Fifteen-second questions

| **6** | Ѝᛠᛠ I |

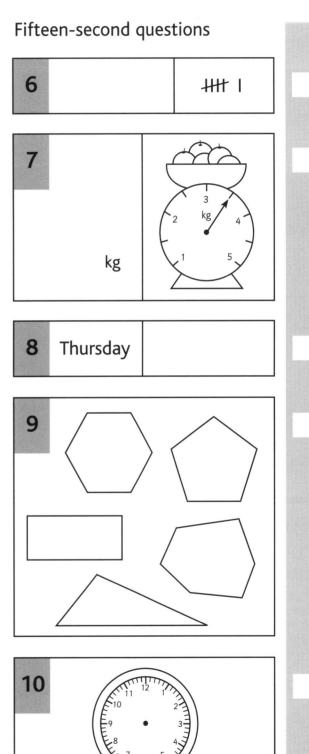

| **7** | kg |

| **8** | Thursday | |

Practice question

	6	5 1

Ten-second questions

1	10	6 4

2	8	14 6

3	12	6 2

4	4	20 16

5	60	20 40

Fifteen-second questions

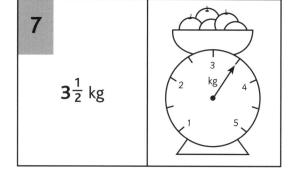

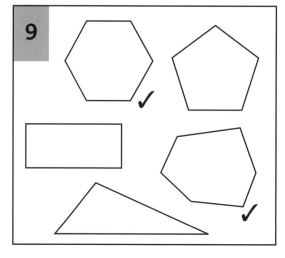

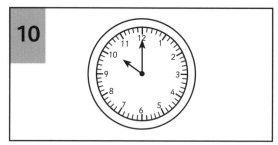

Andrew Brodie: Mental Maths Tests 6–7 © A & C Black

Before playing the test on the CD give each child a copy of the test and read out the following script:

> **Listen to the instructions carefully. I will answer any questions that you have after I have finished reading the instructions to you. Once the test starts you will not be able to ask any questions.**
>
> **The first question is a practice question. In the test there will then be ten questions.**
>
> **Each question has an answer box. Make sure that you only write the answer to the correct question in the box. Try to work out each answer in your head. You can make notes outside the answer box if this helps you but do not try to write out calculations because you will not have enough time. For each question you will find important information already provided for you. This information may be numbers or it could be pictures. Look carefully at the information while you listen to the questions.**
>
> **Each question will be read out twice. Listen carefully then work out your answer. If you cannot do the question, just put a cross. If you make a mistake, do not rub out the wrong answer; cross it out and write the correct answer.**
>
> **Some questions are easy and some are more difficult. Do not worry if you find a question hard; just do your best. I hope that you enjoy the test.**

At this point, answer any questions that the children ask.

> **Now listen carefully to the practice question. You will hear the question twice, then you will have ten seconds to work out and write down the answer.**
>
> > *What is four take away one?*
> >
> > *What is four take away one?*

Allow the children ten seconds to write the answer, then say:

> **Put your pencil down.**

Check that the children have written the answer to the practice question in the practice question answer box. Remind them that they cannot ask any more questions once the test is started. When you are ready, press start on your CD player.

When the test is finished ask the children to stop writing, then collect the test sheets. For ease of marking we have created a copy of the test paper with the answers entered in the appropriate boxes.

Questions for Test 3

For each of the first five questions you have ten seconds to work out and write down the answer.

1   Eighteen subtract four.

2   Add five to nineteen.

3   What number is half of twenty-two?

4   Divide twenty by four.

5   What is double twenty?

For each of the next questions you have fifteen seconds to work out and write down the answer.

6   Look at the number sequence. Write the next number in the sequence.

7   Look at the shape names. They say triangle, cube, square, cylinder, circle. Two of the shapes are solid shapes. Three of the shapes are flat shapes. Tick the names of the solid shapes.

8   Write the number three hundred and fifty-eight.

9   Look at the circle. Shade three quarters of the circle.

10   If I spend sixty pence, how much change would I get from one pound?

Put your pencil down. The test is over.

Andrew Brodie: Mental Maths Tests 6–7 © A & C Black

First name _____   Last name _____

School _____

_____   **Total marks** [ ]

Practice question

	4 1

[ ]

Ten-second questions

1	18 4

[ ]

2	5 19

[ ]

3	22

[ ]

4	20 4

[ ]

5	20

[ ]

Fifteen-second questions

6	3 6 9 12	

[ ]

7	Triangle	
	Cube	
	Square	
	Cylinder	
	Circle	

[ ]

8	
Three hundred and fifty-eight	

[ ]

9	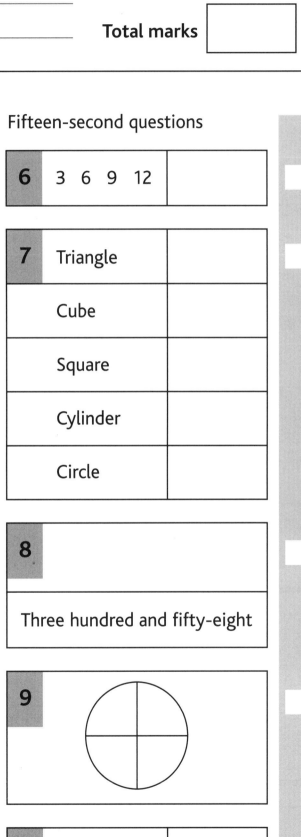

[ ]

10	p	60p £1

[ ]

Practice question

	3	4 1

Ten-second questions

1	**14**	18 4

2	**24**	5 19

3	**11**	22

4	**5**	20 4

5	**40**	20

Fifteen-second questions

6	3 6 9 12	**15**

7	Triangle	
	Cube	✓
	Square	
	Cylinder	✓
	Circle	

8	**358**
	Three hundred and fifty-eight

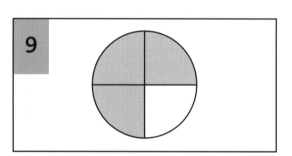

9

10	**40** p	60p £1

Test 4

Before playing the test on the CD give each child a copy of the test and read out the following script:

> **Listen to the instructions carefully. I will answer any questions that you have after I have finished reading the instructions to you. Once the test starts you will not be able to ask any questions.**
>
> **The first question is a practice question. In the test there will then be ten questions.**
>
> **Each question has an answer box. Make sure that you only write the answer to the correct question in the box. Try to work out each answer in your head. You can make notes outside the answer box if this helps you but do not try to write out calculations because you will not have enough time. For each question you will find important information already provided for you. This information may be numbers or it could be pictures. Look carefully at the information while you listen to the questions.**
>
> **Each question will be read out twice. Listen carefully then work out your answer. If you cannot do the question, just put a cross. If you make a mistake, do not rub out the wrong answer; cross it out and write the correct answer.**
>
> **Some questions are easy and some are more difficult. Do not worry if you find a question hard; just do your best. I hope that you enjoy the test.**

At this point, answer any questions that the children ask.

> **Now listen carefully to the practice question. You will hear the question twice, then you will have ten seconds to work out and write down the answer.**
>
> *What is four add three?*
>
> *What is four add three?*

Allow the children ten seconds to write the answer, then say:

> **Put your pencil down.**

Check that the children have written the answer to the practice question in the practice question answer box. Remind them that they cannot ask any more questions once the test is started. When you are ready, press start on your CD player.

When the test is finished ask the children to stop writing, then collect the test sheets. For ease of marking we have created a copy of the test paper with the answers entered in the appropriate boxes.

Questions for Test 4

For each of the first five questions you have ten seconds to work out and write down the answer.

1   How many minutes are there in one hour?

2   Double thirteen.

3   Round sixty-four to the nearest ten.

4   What is the sum of seventeen and six?

5   Take eight from twenty-one.

For each of the next questions you have fifteen seconds to work out and write down the answer.

6   What is the total of six, seven and eight?

7   Look at the shape names. They say pyramid, sphere, star, triangle, square. Two of the shapes are solid shapes. Three of the shapes are flat shapes. Tick the names of the solid shapes.

8   What month follows straight after April?

9   Look at the clock face. Draw the clock hands to show the time seven o'clock.

10   One hundred subtract thirty.

Put your pencil down. The test is over.

Andrew Brodie: Mental Maths Tests 6–7 © A & C Black

Test 4

First name _____ Last name _____

School _____

_____ **Total marks** [　]

Practice question

	4　3

[　]

Ten-second questions

1	minutes	One hour

[　]

2	13

[　]

3	64

[　]

4	17　6

[　]

5	8　21

[　]

Fifteen-second questions

6	6　7　8

[　]

7	Pyramid	
	Sphere	
	Star	
	Triangle	
	Square	

[　]

8	April	

[　]

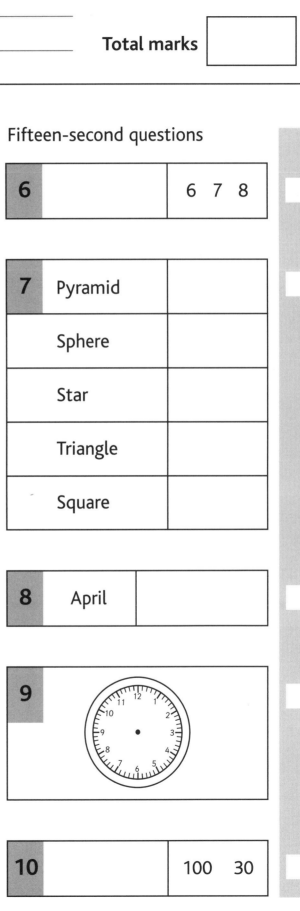

9	

[　]

10	100　30

[　]

Practice question

	7	4 3

Ten-second questions

1	**60** minutes	One hour

2	**26**	13

3	**60**	64

4	**23**	17 6

5	**13**	8 21

Fifteen-second questions

6	**21**	6 7 8

7	Pyramid	✓
	Sphere	✓
	Star	
	Triangle	
	Square	

8	April	**May**

9	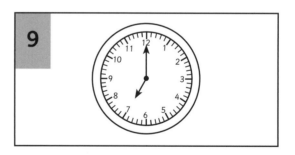

10	**70**	100 30

Before playing the test on the CD give each child a copy of the test and read out the following script:

Listen to the instructions carefully. I will answer any questions that you have after I have finished reading the instructions to you. Once the test starts you will not be able to ask any questions.

The first question is a practice question. In the test there will then be ten questions.

Each question has an answer box. Make sure that you only write the answer to the correct question in the box. Try to work out each answer in your head. You can make notes outside the answer box if this helps you but do not try to write out calculations because you will not have enough time. For each question you will find important information already provided for you. This information may be numbers or it could be pictures. Look carefully at the information while you listen to the questions.

Each question will be read out twice. Listen carefully then work out your answer. If you cannot do the question, just put a cross. If you make a mistake, do not rub out the wrong answer; cross it out and write the correct answer.

Some questions are easy and some are more difficult. Do not worry if you find a question hard; just do your best. I hope that you enjoy the test.

At this point, answer any questions that the children ask.

Now listen carefully to the practice question. You will hear the question twice, then you will have ten seconds to work out and write down the answer.

What is two add one?

What is two add one?

Allow the children ten seconds to write the answer, then say:

Put your pencil down.

Check that the children have written the answer to the practice question in the practice question answer box. Remind them that they cannot ask any more questions once the test is started. When you are ready, press start on your CD player.

When the test is finished ask the children to stop writing, then collect the test sheets. For ease of marking we have created a copy of the test paper with the answers entered in the appropriate boxes.

Questions for Test 5

For each of the first five questions you have ten seconds to work out and write down the answer.

1   What is the difference between thirty and twenty?

2   Divide twelve by three.

3   Add thirteen to six.

4   Forty add thirty.

5   How many minutes are there in half an hour?

For each of the next questions you have fifteen seconds to work out and write down the answer.

6   How many sides does a hexagon have?

7   Look at the scales. Some potatoes are being weighed. What is the weight of the potatoes?

8   Write the number four hundred and ninety-two.

9   Look at the shapes. Write a tick by the pentagon.

10   How many days are there altogether in two weeks?

Put your pencil down. The test is over.

Andrew Brodie: Mental Maths Tests 6–7 © A & C Black

First name _____   Last name _____

School _____

_____   **Total marks** [   ]

Practice question

| | 2 | 1 | ☐ |

Ten-second questions

| 1 | 30 | 20 | ☐ |

| 2 | 12 | 3 | ☐ |

| 3 | 13 | 6 | ☐ |

| 4 | 40 | 30 | ☐ |

| 5 | minutes | Half an hour | ☐ |

Fifteen-second questions

| 6 | hexagon | ☐ |

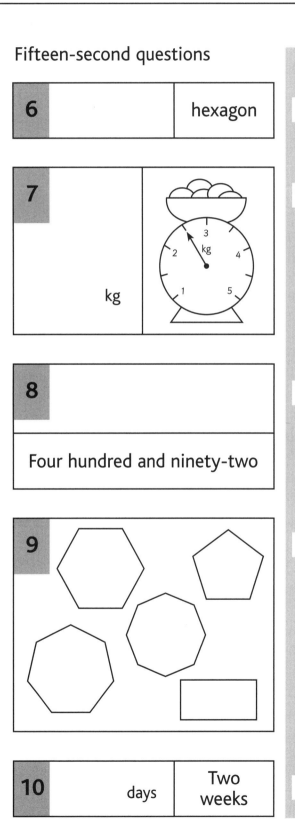

| 7 | kg | ☐ |

| 8 | Four hundred and ninety-two | ☐ |

| 9 | | ☐ |

| 10 | days | Two weeks | ☐ |

Practice question

	3	2	1

Ten-second questions

1	10	30	20

2	4	12	3

3	19	13	6

4	70	40	30

5	30 minutes	Half an hour

Fifteen-second questions

6	6	hexagon

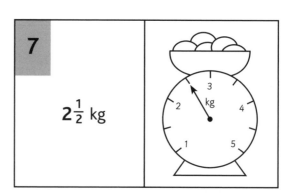

7	$2\frac{1}{2}$ kg

8	492
	Four hundred and ninety-two

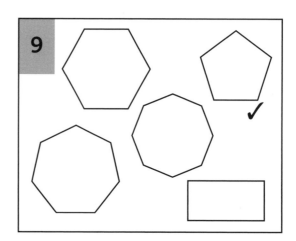

10	14 days	Two weeks

Before playing the test on the CD give each child a copy of the test and read out the following script:

Listen to the instructions carefully. I will answer any questions that you have after I have finished reading the instructions to you. Once the test starts you will not be able to ask any questions.

The first question is a practice question. In the test there will then be ten questions.

Each question has an answer box. Make sure that you only write the answer to the correct question in the box. Try to work out each answer in your head. You can make notes outside the answer box if this helps you but do not try to write out calculations because you will not have enough time. For each question you will find important information already provided for you. This information may be numbers or it could be pictures. Look carefully at the information while you listen to the questions.

Each question will be read out twice. Listen carefully then work out your answer. If you cannot do the question, just put a cross. If you make a mistake, do not rub out the wrong answer; cross it out and write the correct answer.

Some questions are easy and some are more difficult. Do not worry if you find a question hard; just do your best. I hope that you enjoy the test.

At this point, answer any questions that the children ask.

Now listen carefully to the practice question. You will hear the question twice, then you will have ten seconds to work out and write down the answer.

What is five add two?

What is five add two?

Allow the children ten seconds to write the answer, then say:

Put your pencil down.

Check that the children have written the answer to the practice question in the practice question answer box. Remind them that they cannot ask any more questions once the test is started. When you are ready, press start on your CD player.

When the test is finished ask the children to stop writing, then collect the test sheets. For ease of marking we have created a copy of the test paper with the answers entered in the appropriate boxes.

Questions for Test 6

For each of the first five questions you have ten seconds to work out and write down the answer.

1   How much more is twenty than thirteen?

2   What is seven times two?

3   Sixteen plus eight.

4   Divide twelve by two.

5   How many minutes are there in half an hour?

For each of the next questions you have fifteen seconds to work out and write down the answer.

6   Look at the clock face. Draw the clock hands to show the time half past ten.

7   Look at the tally. What total does it show?

8   Look at the square. Shade three quarters of the square.

9   What month comes immediately before July?

10   Find the total of five, eight and six.

Put your pencil down. The test is over.

Andrew Brodie: Mental Maths Tests 6–7 © A & C Black

Test 6

First name _____ Last name _____

School _____

_____ **Total marks** [   ]

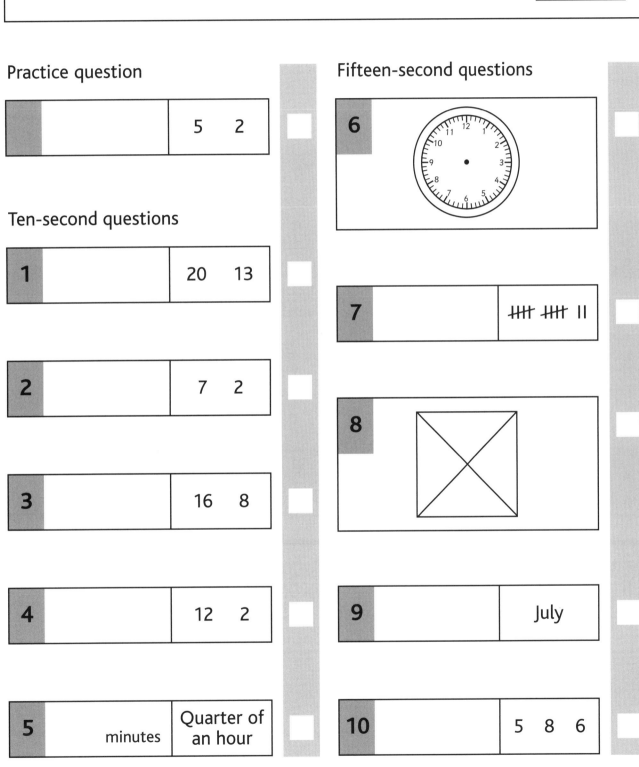

Practice question

	5 2

Ten-second questions

1	20 13	☐
2	7 2	☐
3	16 8	☐
4	12 2	☐
5	minutes	Quarter of an hour	☐

Fifteen-second questions

6	(clock)	☐
7	＝ ＝ II	☐
8	(square with diagonals)	☐
9	July	☐
10	5 8 6	☐

Practice question

7	5 2

Ten-second questions

1	7	20 13

2	14	7 2

3	24	16 8

4	6	12 2

5	15 minutes	Quarter of an hour

Fifteen-second questions

7	12	҂Ӈ ҂Ӈ II

9	June	July

10	19	5 8 6

Andrew Brodie: Mental Maths Tests 6–7 © A & C Black

Test 7

Before playing the test on the CD give each child a copy of the test and read out the following script:

> **Listen to the instructions carefully. I will answer any questions that you have after I have finished reading the instructions to you. Once the test starts you will not be able to ask any questions.**
>
> **The first question is a practice question. In the test there will then be ten questions.**
>
> **Each question has an answer box. Make sure that you only write the answer to the correct question in the box. Try to work out each answer in your head. You can make notes outside the answer box if this helps you but do not try to write out calculations because you will not have enough time. For each question you will find important information already provided for you. This information may be numbers or it could be pictures. Look carefully at the information while you listen to the questions.**
>
> **Each question will be read out twice. Listen carefully then work out your answer. If you cannot do the question, just put a cross. If you make a mistake, do not rub out the wrong answer; cross it out and write the correct answer.**
>
> **Some questions are easy and some are more difficult. Do not worry if you find a question hard; just do your best. I hope that you enjoy the test.**

At this point, answer any questions that the children ask.

> **Now listen carefully to the practice question. You will hear the question twice, then you will have ten seconds to work out and write down the answer.**
>
> > *What is three add three?*
> >
> > *What is three add three?*

Allow the children ten seconds to write the answer, then say:

> **Put your pencil down.**

Check that the children have written the answer to the practice question in the practice question answer box. Remind them that they cannot ask any more questions once the test is started. When you are ready, press start on your CD player.

When the test is finished ask the children to stop writing, then collect the test sheets. For ease of marking we have created a copy of the test paper with the answers entered in the appropriate boxes.

Questions for Test 7

For each of the first five questions you have ten seconds to work out and write down the answer.

1   What number is double twelve?

2   Round eighty-eight to the nearest ten.

3   Look at the numbers. Draw a ring around the odd number.

4   Thirty subtract seven.

5   What is eight times five?

For each of the next questions you have fifteen seconds to work out and write down the answer.

6   Look at the clock face. Draw the clock hands to show the time half past four.

7   Look at the shapes. Write a tick by the octagon.

8   Write the number five hundred and twenty.

9   Look at the number sequence. Write the next number in the sequence.

10   What month follows straight after February?

Put your pencil down. The test is over.

Test 7

First name _____   Last name _____

School _____

_____   **Total marks** [   ]

Practice question

	3 3

Ten-second questions

1	12

2	88

3	14 18 12 17 30

4	30 7

5	8 5

Fifteen-second questions

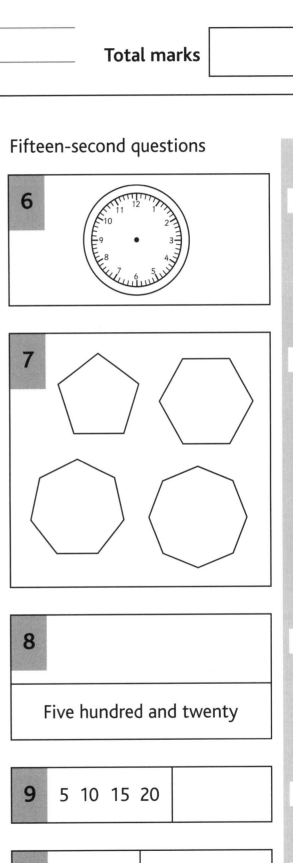

6

7

8   Five hundred and twenty

9	5 10 15 20	

10	February	

Practice question

6	3	3

Ten-second questions

1	**24**	12

2	**90**	88

3	14 18 12 ⑰ 30

4	**23**	30 7

5	**40**	8 5

Fifteen-second questions

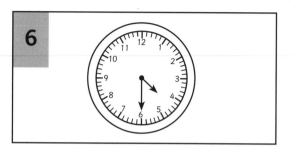

6	

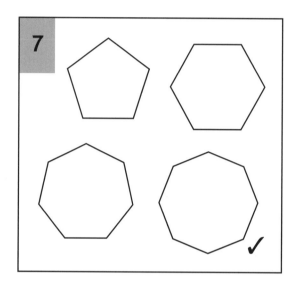

7	

8	**520**
	Five hundred and twenty

9	5 10 15 20	**25**

10	February	**March**

Test 8

Before playing the test on the CD give each child a copy of the test and read out the following script:

> **Listen to the instructions carefully. I will answer any questions that you have after I have finished reading the instructions to you. Once the test starts you will not be able to ask any questions.**
>
> **The first question is a practice question. In the test there will then be ten questions.**
>
> **Each question has an answer box. Make sure that you only write the answer to the correct question in the box. Try to work out each answer in your head. You can make notes outside the answer box if this helps you but do not try to write out calculations because you will not have enough time. For each question you will find important information already provided for you. This information may be numbers or it could be pictures. Look carefully at the information while you listen to the questions.**
>
> **Each question will be read out twice. Listen carefully then work out your answer. If you cannot do the question, just put a cross. If you make a mistake, do not rub out the wrong answer; cross it out and write the correct answer.**
>
> **Some questions are easy and some are more difficult. Do not worry if you find a question hard; just do your best. I hope that you enjoy the test.**

At this point, answer any questions that the children ask.

> **Now listen carefully to the practice question. You will hear the question twice, then you will have ten seconds to work out and write down the answer.**
>
> > *What is six subtract two?*
> >
> > *What is six subtract two?*

Allow the children ten seconds to write the answer, then say:

> **Put your pencil down.**

Check that the children have written the answer to the practice question in the practice question answer box. Remind them that they cannot ask any more questions once the test is started. When you are ready, press start on your CD player.

When the test is finished ask the children to stop writing, then collect the test sheets. For ease of marking we have created a copy of the test paper with the answers entered in the appropriate boxes.

For each of the first five questions you have ten seconds to work out and write down the answer.

1   What is fifty add thirty?

2   Twelve minus four.

3   What number is half of thirty?

4   Look at the numbers. Draw a ring around the even number.

5   Divide eighteen by two.

For each of the next questions you have fifteen seconds to work out and write down the answer.

6   If I buy a pen for seventy-five pence, what change will I have from one pound?

7   Add together seven, nine and eleven.

8   Look at the square. What fraction of the square is shaded?

9   Look at the clock face. Draw the clock hands to show the time a quarter past six.

10   Look at the line and the ruler. How long is the line to the nearest centimetre?

Put your pencil down. The test is over.

Andrew Brodie: Mental Maths Tests 6–7 © A & C Black

Test 8

First name _____ Last name _____

School _____

_____ **Total marks** [ ]

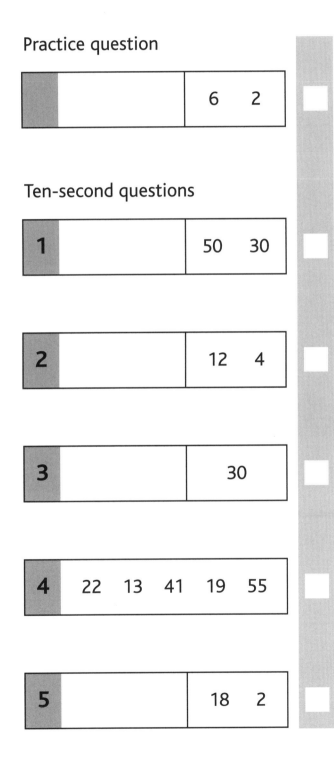

Practice question

| | 6 2 | □ |

Ten-second questions

1	50 30	□
2	12 4	□
3	30	□
4	22 13 41 19 55	□
5	18 2	□

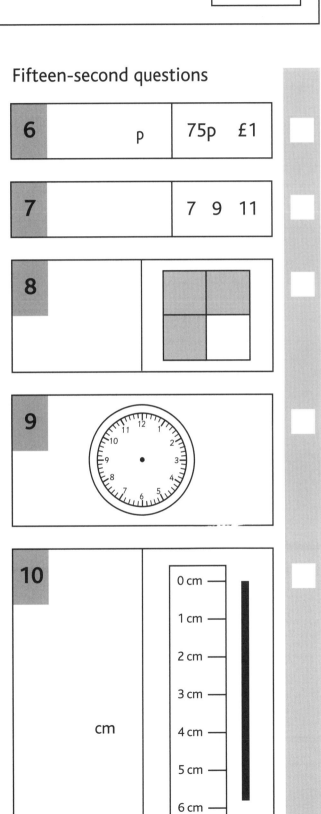

Fifteen-second questions

6	p	75p £1	□
7		7 9 11	□
8			□
9			□
10	cm		□

Practice question

	4	6 2

Ten-second questions

1	80	50 30

2	8	12 4

3	15	30

4	(22) 13 41 19 55

5	9	18 2

Fifteen-second questions

6	25 p	75p £1

7	27	7 9 11

8	$\frac{3}{4}$	

9	

10	6 cm	

Andrew Brodie: Mental Maths Tests 6–7 © A & C Black

Test 9

Before playing the test on the CD give each child a copy of the test and read out the following script:

Listen to the instructions carefully. I will answer any questions that you have after I have finished reading the instructions to you. Once the test starts you will not be able to ask any questions.

The first question is a practice question. In the test there will then be ten questions.

Each question has an answer box. Make sure that you only write the answer to the correct question in the box. Try to work out each answer in your head. You can make notes outside the answer box if this helps you but do not try to write out calculations because you will not have enough time. For each question you will find important information already provided for you. This information may be numbers or it could be pictures. Look carefully at the information while you listen to the questions.

Each question will be read out twice. Listen carefully then work out your answer. If you cannot do the question, just put a cross. If you make a mistake, do not rub out the wrong answer; cross it out and write the correct answer.

Some questions are easy and some are more difficult. Do not worry if you find a question hard; just do your best. I hope that you enjoy the test.

At this point, answer any questions that the children ask.

Now listen carefully to the practice question. You will hear the question twice, then you will have ten seconds to work out and write down the answer.

> *What is four minus one?*

> *What is four minus one?*

Allow the children ten seconds to write the answer, then say:

Put your pencil down.

Check that the children have written the answer to the practice question in the practice question answer box. Remind them that they cannot ask any more questions once the test is started. When you are ready, press start on your CD player.

When the test is finished ask the children to stop writing, then collect the test sheets. For ease of marking we have created a copy of the test paper with the answers entered in the appropriate boxes.

Questions for Test 9

For each of the first five questions you have ten seconds to work out and write down the answer.

1 Add sixteen to forty.

2 What is the difference between twenty-three and thirty?

3 What number is double seventeen?

4 Multiply five by nine.

5 Share sixteen between two.

For each of the next questions you have fifteen seconds to work out and write down the answer.

6 Look at the clock face. Draw the clock hands to show the time a quarter past nine.

7 Look at the numbers. Draw rings around the multiples of ten.

8 I buy a pencil for 40p and a ruler for 30p. What change do I have from £1?

9 Look at the circle. What fraction of the circle is shaded?

10 Write the number seven hundred and forty-five.

Put your pencil down. The test is over.

Andrew Brodie: Mental Maths Tests 6–7 © A & C Black

Test 9

First name _____   Last name _____

School _____

_____   **Total marks** [ ]

Practice question

	4 1

[ ]

Ten-second questions

1	16 40

[ ]

2	23 30

[ ]

3	17

[ ]

4	5 9

[ ]

5	16 2

[ ]

Fifteen-second questions

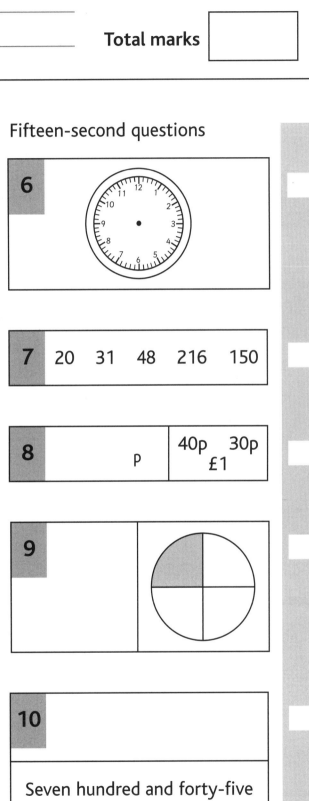

6	(clock face)

[ ]

7	20 31 48 216 150

[ ]

8	p	40p 30p £1

[ ]

9	(circle, one quarter shaded)

[ ]

10	
Seven hundred and forty-five	

[ ]

Practice question

3	4 1

Ten-second questions

Fifteen-second questions

1	56	16 40

6	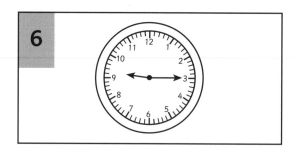

2	7	23 30

7	(20) 31 48 216 (150)

3	34	17

8	30p	40p 30p £1

4	45	5 9

9	$\frac{1}{4}$	(circle with one quarter shaded)

5	8	16 2

10	745
	Seven hundred and forty-five

Andrew Brodie: Mental Maths Tests 6–7 © A & C Black

Before playing the test on the CD give each child a copy of the test and read out the following script:

> **Listen to the instructions carefully. I will answer any questions that you have after I have finished reading the instructions to you. Once the test starts you will not be able to ask any questions.**
>
> **The first question is a practice question. In the test there will then be ten questions.**
>
> **Each question has an answer box. Make sure that you only write the answer to the correct question in the box. Try to work out each answer in your head. You can make notes outside the answer box if this helps you but do not try to write out calculations because you will not have enough time. For each question you will find important information already provided for you. This information may be numbers or it could be pictures. Look carefully at the information while you listen to the questions.**
>
> **Each question will be read out twice. Listen carefully then work out your answer. If you cannot do the question, just put a cross. If you make a mistake, do not rub out the wrong answer; cross it out and write the correct answer.**
>
> **Some questions are easy and some are more difficult. Do not worry if you find a question hard; just do your best. I hope that you enjoy the test.**

At this point, answer any questions that the children ask.

> **Now listen carefully to the practice question. You will hear the question twice, then you will have ten seconds to work out and write down the answer.**
>
> *What is eight add two?*
>
> *What is eight add two?*

Allow the children ten seconds to write the answer, then say:

> **Put your pencil down.**

Check that the children have written the answer to the practice question in the practice question answer box. Remind them that they cannot ask any more questions once the test is started. When you are ready, press start on your CD player.

When the test is finished ask the children to stop writing, then collect the test sheets. For ease of marking we have created a copy of the test paper with the answers entered in the appropriate boxes.

For each of the first five questions you have ten seconds to work out and write down the answer.

1	Look at the numbers. Draw a ring around the even number.
2	Find half of forty-two.
3	What is six times five?
4	How much more is fifty pounds than twenty pounds?
5	Round one hundred and forty-seven to the nearest ten.

For each of the next questions you have fifteen seconds to work out and write down the answer.

6	What day follows straight after Saturday?
7	Add together thirty, forty and fifty.
8	Look at the shape. Write the name of the shape.
9	How many days are there altogether in three weeks?
10	Look at the line and the ruler. How long is the line to the nearest centimetre?

Put your pencil down. The test is over.

Andrew Brodie: Mental Maths Tests 6–7 © A & C Black

Test 10

First name _____   Last name _____

School _____

_____   **Total marks** [   ]

Practice question

	8 2

[ ]

Ten-second questions

1	29 30 31 33 41

[ ]

2	42

[ ]

3	6 5

[ ]

4	£	£50 £20

[ ]

5	147

[ ]

Fifteen-second questions

6	Saturday	

[ ]

7		30 40 50

[ ]

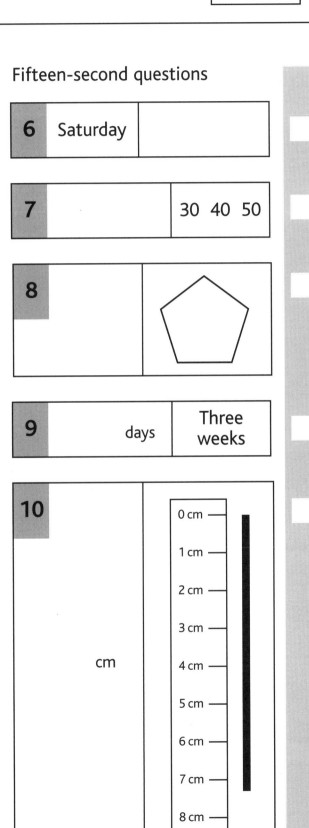

8	

[ ]

9	days	Three weeks

[ ]

10	cm	

[ ]

Practice question

	10	8 2

Ten-second questions

1	29 (30) 31 33 41

2	21	42

3	30	6 5

4	£ 30	£50 £20

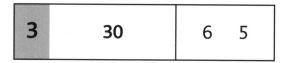

5	150	147

Fifteen-second questions

6	Saturday	**Sunday**

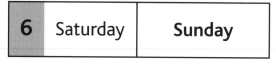

7	120	30 40 50

8	**Pentagon**	

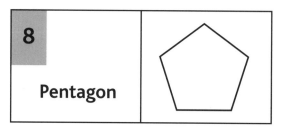

9	**21** days	Three weeks

10	**7** cm	

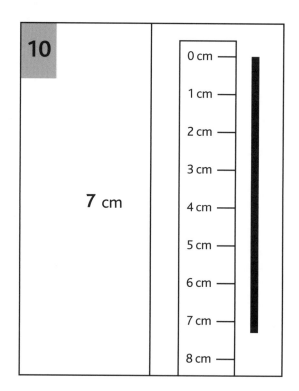

Andrew Brodie: Mental Maths Tests 6–7 © A & C Black

Pupil record sheet

You may wish to record your pupils' scores as they complete each test.

Page 44 consists of a record sheet on which you can enter the pupils' names down the left hand column and the dates of the tests along the top. On page 45 there is a graph for recording the scores for each individual pupil. By photocopying this sheet for every member of the class you can monitor each individual's progress from test to test.

It is worth observing where the pupils are making errors. Errors may occur on particular types of questions, perhaps where certain vocabulary is used. Is there a pattern to their problems?

You may also find that some pupils find the time restrictions challenging. Do they find the ten-second questions more difficult, for example, simply due to the speed with which they have to answer?

Where patterns do emerge you will be able to target your teaching to address the pupils' needs. You should then find improvements as the pupils work through the set of tests.

Pages 46 to 48 provide some extra mental arithmetic practice.

Pupil Record Sheet

Class _____

Test number:	1	2	3	4	5	6	7	8	9	10
Date:										
Name:										

Pupil Progress Graph

Name _____

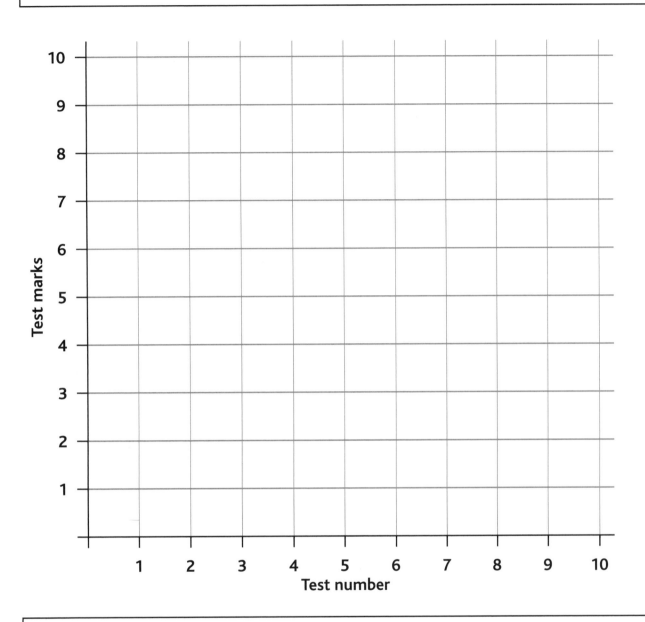

Test marks (y-axis: 1 to 10)

Test number (x-axis: 1 to 10)

Comments, including any particular areas of difficulty

Practice page

Draw hands to show the correct times on the clocks.

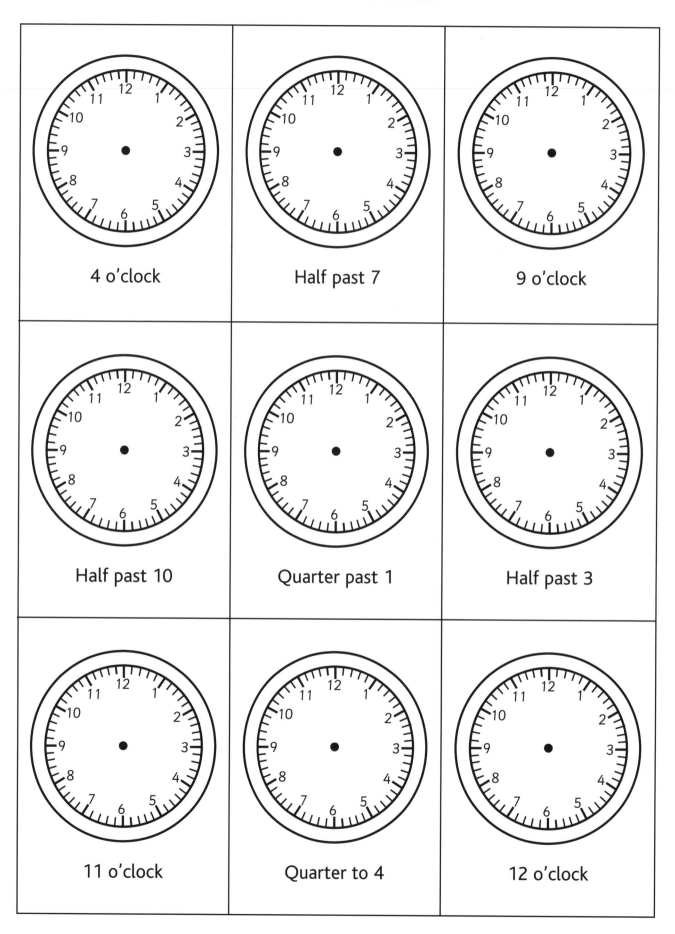

4 o'clock	Half past 7	9 o'clock
Half past 10	Quarter past 1	Half past 3
11 o'clock	Quarter to 4	12 o'clock

Andrew Brodie: Mental Maths Tests 6–7 © A & C Black

Practice page

Here is a hundred square.

Colour all the even numbers.

1	2	3	4	5	6	7	8	9	10
11	12	13	14	15	16	17	18	19	20
21	22	23	24	25	26	27	28	29	30
31	32	33	34	35	36	37	38	39	40
41	42	43	44	45	46	47	48	49	50
51	52	53	54	55	56	57	58	59	60
61	62	63	64	65	66	67	68	69	70
71	72	73	74	75	76	77	78	79	80
81	82	83	84	85	86	87	88	89	90
91	92	93	94	95	96	97	98	99	100

Which is the smallest even number?

Which is the smallest odd number?

Practice page

How quickly can you find the doubles and the halves?

Quick doubles	Quick halves
Double 6 =	Half of 30 =
Double 9 =	Half of 40 =
Double 12 =	Half of 80 =
Double 10 =	Half of 100 =
Double 15 =	Half of 20 =
Double 8 =	Half of 50 =
Double 4 =	Half of 70 =
Double 13 =	Half of 16 =
Double 1 =	Half of 12 =
Double 16 =	Half of 18 =
Double 20 =	Half of 24 =
Double 7 =	Half of 90 =
Double 25 =	Half of 28 =
Double 3 =	Half of 14 =
Double 18 =	Half of 32 =